PRESIDENT BILL

A GRAPHIC EPIC
by
WILLIAM L. BROWN
★
Foreword
by
JULES FEIFFER

For information write Andrews and McMeel, a Universal Press Syndicate Company, 4900 Main Street, Kansas City, Missouri 64112.

ISBN: 0-8362-7984-0

Library of Congress Catalog Card Number: 90-82680

Randomocratists, become an official Loyal Constituent of President Bill! Send a stamped, self-addressed, legal-sized envelope to:

President Bill
PO Box 5216
Takoma Park, Maryland 20913-0216

Foreword

We all know how George Bush is screwing things up, but if you're so smart what would you do if *you* were president? It is to this challenge, common to the musings of us all, that William L. Brown rises in his whimsical series of satiric panels, *President Bill*.

Brown, a child of New Hampshire, is presently a graphic artist in residence in Takoma Park, a suburb of our nation's capital, made up in abundant numbers of postgraduates of the Woodstock generation. No longer are they levitating the Pentagon. Now, in this time of international upheaval and domestic lassitude, they lounge in coffee shops and playgrounds, wearing backpacks of baby bottles, baby wipes, and biodegradable diapers. And they push strollers full of the next generation of thwarted hopefuls, due to commence protesting some twenty years hence, in the decade which will no doubt be labeled by the media of its day as "the Tens."

The palaver of these post-hippie parents is a good-humored mix of beltway politics and child care. One can imagine Bill Brown taking it all in and saying to himself, "What if—?"

President Bill is more a satire of Bill Brown's kind than George Bush's. And therein lies its freshness and brilliance. Brown's deadpan text and smartly observed drawings display an affectionately ironic vision of the politics and behavior of his friends and neighbors in the seat of power. The woodcutty-appearing cartoons are executed on scratch board in perfect comic representation of middle-class bohemia: sneakers, sandals, sweatshirts, jeans, beer and more beer, toddlers and infants and moms' bellies swollen with the promise of another population explosion. Bemused, confused, smug and well-meaning, messy and environmentally passionate, Brown's folk prove to be nearly as dangerous but infinitely more human than Bush's or Reagan's folk before them.

Read through these pages and see presidential limos recycled into windmill parts. See a Secret Service forced to follow the chief of state around on bicycles (which works out fine, since interstate highways are to be replaced by solar-powered transit lines). See our vegetarian president celebrate the National Turnip.

President Bill runs in the *City Paper*, a local alternative weekly in suburban D.C., where it began in the spring of '88. Since then, it has picked up a few more papers and a lot more fans. This collection should add considerably to that number.

I am pleased and flattered to have been asked to write this introduction, in that my wife's sister, Cindy, and her husband, Larry, full-familied citizens of Takoma Park (Lincoln and Luke and one on the way) are, respectively, Director of the Delaware River Basin Commission and Chief Negotiator in the administration of President Bill. More than thirty years in this business has taught me, it never hurts to suck up to power.

JULES FEIFFER
Martha's Vineyard
August 1990

Author's note: Jules Feiffer has been appointed governor of our 51st state, Martha's Vineyard. WLB

Dedicated to Mary, Adair, and Austin,
who believed in me
even when they didn't believe me.

PRESIDENT BILL

How did I get to ★ ★ ★ be president? I won the lottery, that's how! I was the winner of the first Presidential Selection lottery. The Presidential Selection was established by a Constitutional Convention when a rogue delegation sold its swing-vote on the Balanced Budget Amendment for support on its election reform. Like everyone else on Selection Day I was having a beer, watching Miss Selectoral College draw the winning social security number, and it was mine. Mine!

PRESIDENT BILL

My friends were as shocked as everybody else when they learned I had been selected president. They were happy for us and, at first, we talked about all the parties and dances we would have at the White House. We promised all our friends with children they could come to the Easter Egg Hunt. Also, I offered the use of the White House for Thursday-night practices for my Morris team. But, as the date of the Inauguration approached, my friends started acting strangely.

fter I was selected to be president in the lottery, I was briefed by official advisors from the Selectoral College. They told me my Inaugural Address should be upbeat, middle-of-the-road, bipartisan, and confidence-building. They even offered to have it written for me by their staff speech-writers. I thanked them politely, but said I'd rather do it myself. That was fine, they said, and perhaps I'd like them to proofread it for me when I finished. They looked worried when I refused. ★ ★

① PRESIDENT BILL ②

I should explain about my wife, Mary, and me. We get along most of the time, better than a lot of married people, really. It's just that she gets real cranky, and rather critical, when she hasn't eaten for a while, which she hadn't. Also, she does tend to be more conservative than I. So, I can't blame her for letting off steam once we got to the White House and had snuck off alone to a little room full of chairs facing a dais. But, I still say it was her fault for not checking to see if the microphone was live before she said all those things. ★ ★ ★

How could you? You threatened the life of the former president! In your inauguration speech! I've never been so embarrassed. Not to mention I've had to care for the baby myself the ENTIRE day!

PRESS ROOM RULES

PRESS

BRIE ROO

PRESIDENT BILL

At the first press conference of my administration, I spoke for two hours, outlining my policy goals. I described in detail our plans to nationalize industry, gut defense, re-distribute wealth, replace cars with mass transit, and convert the nation to solar power. I stressed that we were determined not to treat the press superficially or manipulatively. "We will not treat the American public as if they were fools. We will not treat the American press as a tool of the government," I said. Then I opened the floor to questions, "the harder, the better." ★ ★

PRESIDENT BILL

My official advisors, ★ congress-people, and my friends pressed me to choose a Cabinet as soon as possible. Each gave me a list of highly qualified candidates. I decided to pick my Cabinet in the same spirit of pure democratic-equality in which I had been chosen president -- random selection. It was the fairest, most objective way I could think of. Using the same method I once saw in an old movie, I emptied a fountain pen over the flipping pages of a phone book. The names on which the spots of ink fell would be the members of my cabinet. ★ ★

thought better of my first impulse to choose my cabinet at random. If I was to effectively initiate a visionary new national agenda, I needed a group of talented, experienced, and, above all, loyal people. Following tradition, I chose from my friends and family. I have a lot of friends and a big family. So, also following tradition, I made a few additions to the cabinet departments. These changes reflected my administration's progressive priorities. For instance, I created a cabinet post for women and one for each ★ minority. ★ ★ ★

11

PRESIDENT BILL

My administration was to be guided by a strict sense of right and wrong. I swore we would never use military force except to defend the borders. But sometimes past wrongs must be righted, whatever the cost. In 1973 there was a coup, supported by the US government and corporations against the elected socialist government of Chile. The Chilean president was gunned down. Political parties, organizations, and unions were disbanded, their members murdered, tortured, and jailed. General Augusto Pinochet Ugarte proclaimed himself president. ★ ★

M⊙ PRESIDENT BILL ⊗

My plan to persuade ★ General Pinochet to leave office and return Chile to democratic rule went somewhat askew. The Air Force missed the Chilean presidential residence, instead slightly bombing the nearby neighborhood, killing 158 civilians, and wounding hundreds more, including two Soviet diplomats. Congress condemned the attack, as did the United Nations. The Soviet Union sent a nasty note, and my State Department advisors urged me to adopt more subtle means of encouraging reform in Chile, perhaps through diplomatic or economic incentives.

13

PRESIDENT BILL

Though I appointed my friends and family to every administration post down to the Director of the American Battle Monuments Commission, one position remained conspicuously vacant; the vice-presidency. My good friend, and Secretary of State, Dan, counseled me on the matter. There are two approaches, he said, the first is to appoint a worthy successor, a popular leader, a capable person, someone who would carry on my political programs -- should I be "unable." Then, he said, there's the second approach . . . ★ ★ ★ ★ ★ ★ ★ ★ ★ ★ ★ ★ ★ ★

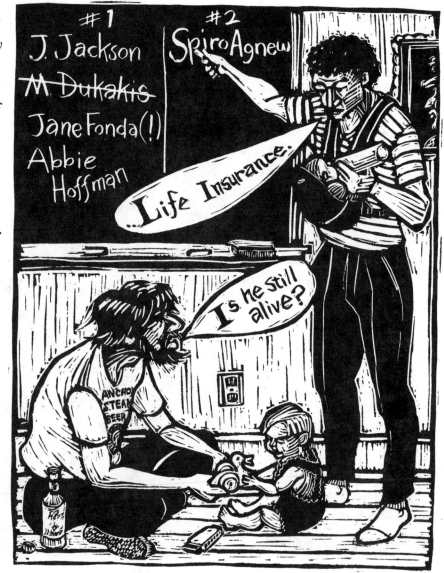

PRESIDENT BILL

Picking a vice ★ ★ ★ president was difficult, despite all the advice from friends, the Cabinet, Congress-people, special-interest groups, editors, columnists, talk-show hosts, and public-opinion polls. Most of the advice amounted to, "Pick me or my friend, here!" My cabinet members even began coveting the position, though it provided almost no real power. But, then, it was only a heartbeat away from ALL the power. They constantly urged me to decide. As long as I put it off, they said, the nation and randomocracy were in peril. ★ ★ ★ ★ ★

◇ ⊚ PRESIDENT BILL ⊗

Once again, the ★ ★ ★ practice of randomocracy (government through random-selection) came down on the side of justice, equality, and absolute fairness. Who could have asked for a better vice-president than she who was selected by chance? Evita, our day-care provider, was a working-class, Hispanic woman, a perfect symbol of the people my administration strove to represent and champion. It really was perfect since, unlike most vice-presidents, she wouldn't be hanging around with nothing to do -- she had full-time day-care duties.

◎ PRESIDENT BILL ⊗

*C*hoosing a vice- ★ ★ ★ president by picking the first person who walks in the door leaves no opportunity to do a background check. Evita, my Vice-President/Child-Care Provider was an illegal alien, but that didn't bother me, though it upset some legal-eagle types, nitpicking about constitutional requirements. However, it came out that Evita misled us in order to get her child-care job. She intimated that her family fled to the United States escaping right-wing death-squads. It was because of their involvement in a certain organization, she said.

PRESIDENT BILL

I decreed that the ★ ★ White House provide models of self-sufficiency, conservation, and alternative energy sources. As my appointees -- especially Paul, an anti-nuclear power activist, now Secretary of Energy -- assumed their duties, the grounds of the Executive Mansion soon took on a fresh appearance, what with the Executive Recycling Center, Solar Panels, Windmills, Sheep Herd, Milk Cow, Organic Garden, Compost Heap, and also the Secretary of Energy's teepee, his girlfriend's outdoor batik studio, and their outhouse. ★ ★ ★ ★ ★

PRESIDENT BILL

I had the presidential limousines scrapped and recycled into wind-mill parts. The chauffeurs were reassigned to the Transportation Department's National Mass Transit Decontruction Corps, the agency designated to tear up the interstate highways. The roads would be replaced with a solar-powered interurban rail transit system (as soon as it was developed). Meanwhile, as part of our "Is This Trip Eco-Logical?" campaign, I was setting an example by using the existing rail system for (necessary) trips, and using my own car as infrequently as possible.

PRESIDENT BILL

Mine was not to be an imperial presidency. The First Family tried to retain its old values and way of life. Most of the Executive Mansion's household staff was reassigned. We drove our own vehicles and, at first, did our own chores: cooking, cleaning, and shopping. However, the cleaning was especially difficult in such a large house, so we had to bend our principles a little. But, then, politics is compromise. Still, I insisted on setting an example as often as possible. For instance, we shopped at the same stores we always had.

★ ★ ★ ★ ★ ★ ★ ★ ★ ★ ★

PRESIDENT BILL

I recalled how the Nixon White House was bugged. They said the microphones were removed, but how did I know? Think of all the people who might bug the White House; the KGB, for one. And, if the CIA and FBI knew about the KGB bugs, they'd want their own so they'd know what the Soviets knew. And what about the less famous U.S. intelligence agencies, like Army Intelligence, and Navy Intelligence? Undoubtedly, there were many agencies; military, foreign, even corporate, with the capability to plant a mike just about anywhere.

T ◉ PRESIDENT BILL ⊗

Tired of the alienating atmosphere of the White House, we took an extended "vacation," moving back home to Takoma Park. That city is one of Washington, D.C.'s oldest and closest suburbs. For the last two decades it has attracted many activists, musicians, and artisans. It is one of the most racially integrated communities in the D.C. area, and it is, by city ordinance, a Nuclear Free Zone. We would be more comfortable there, surrounded by our own kind; people whose ideals were forged in the crucible of the sixties, people who would support my administration. ★ ★ ★

PRESIDENT BILL

I could propose any program I wished, but only Congress could enact it. I needed a majority of friends and allies there, and to achieve this there were a few obstacles to overcome. My administration had no party affiliation, and little mainstream political experience. Also Congress had unanimously denounced my proposed programs as "degenerate, harebrained nihilism." So, I made the usual presidential gesture of good will and obsequience, I went to Capitol Hill to meet with Congress. I arranged a special escort. ★ ★

PRESIDENT BILL

My negotiations with ★ Congress were straightforward. I warned them that certain radical elements in my Justice Department were urging me to proceed against Congress through the courts. It seems they felt a strong case could be made that the congressional electoral-system is undemocratic. Just look, I said, at the makeup of Congress -- predominantly male, white, and rich -- hardly representative. Our lawyers feel, I said, that only a lottery system, such as the one which selected me as president, would be truly equal, fair, and representative.

⊙ PRESIDENT BILL ⊗

Negotiating with Congress was the easy part. Next I had to negotiate with Mary. I told her I wouldn't be able to evenly split child-care duties with her for a while. Now that Congress was co-operating, I would be extremely busy planning and implementing the details of my administration's programs. I expected to be working late nights in the Oval Office, and traveling to far-off parts of the country. I knew it violated our equal-parenting arrangement, I said, but the country needed me. She said there was only one problem . . . ★ ★ ★

PRESIDENT BILL

Naming my wife to be Chief of Staff was controversial. But, both of us felt strongly that the traditional First Lady position was sexist and belittling. Many First Ladies have been more than capable of holding a Cabinet-level post. Mary was certainly no exception. Critics said Mary was not experienced in politics, that she would not be able to deal with Congress. However, we soon found that even the cynical, worldly horse-traders on Capitol Hill respected Motherhood, especially when brought face-to-face with it. ✦ ✦

PRESIDENT BILL

Having negotiated ★ ★ support from Congress, my administration started enacting its programs with little legislative opposition. First we passed a budget. Our critics had been saying we would never be able to afford to fund all our proposals. But, it was easy. We simply exchanged the budgets, facilities, and equipment of the Defense Department, which was renamed Defense and Urban Maintenance (DUM), with the Environmental Protection Agency, now the Environmental Protection Army. ★

★ ★ ★ ★ ★ ★ ★ ★ ★ ★ ★

PRESIDENT BILL

I am proud of my roots in New Hampshire. My favorite state is blemished only by the fact that most of its citizens are reactionary, provincial Republicans with a habit of electing right-wing, crank governors. There was Meldrim Thompson, who put "live free or die" on the license plates, and John Sununu, who rabidly supported the Seabrook nuclear power plant. That was why I recruited most of the staff of a N.H. anti-nuclear group, the Clamshell Alliance, into my Energy Department and EPA. And, that was why I joined them one night around a cheery bonfire.

PRESIDENT BILL

Yasser Arafat was ★★ invited to speak at the UN, so I had the State Department rush him a visa and an invitation to stay with the First Family in Washington. The reactionary press made its usual fuss over nothing -- just because I met Arafat at the airport and carried his bags to the car for him. Those sensation-seeking journalists would have changed their tone had they spent time with the man as I did. I found him to be intelligent and warm-hearted. After a day of political meetings he loved nothing more than the company of children. ★ ★ ★ ★

29

PRESIDENT BILL

My first meeting with ★ Mikhail Gorbachev was in New York. He was there to address the U.N., but also to meet the new president. After a U.N. speech in which he all but declared the Cold War over, I told him that our countries were now closer than ever, what with perestroika in the East and randomocracy in the West. I said I'd scrap SDI, arms, bases, and Third-World debts, provided he would reciprocate. And, don't worry about verification, I said, I trusted him. Personally, we found the Gorbachevs engaging, and soon we were talking like old friends. ★ ★ ★ ★

PRESIDENT BILL

Holidays are a time to celebrate the old traditions, the very old traditions, the ones observed by our ancestors before missionaries imposed a certain Judaean cult on them. First we changed the national holiday from the 25th to the 21st of December, the Solstice. On that day we torched the National Yule Log to make the National Bonfire, accompanied by a ritual fertility dance, all televised. In the old days they would have slaughtered an ox for a feast, but as many in my administration, myself included, were vegetarians, we made a substitution.

Now, as the National Men's Morris Team dances behind him, the President holds aloft the National Turnip.

PRESIDENT BILL

tan, my Secretary of Housing and Urban Development had previous government experience. He was a park ranger, taking graduate courses in agricultural engineering. I picked him because he had built his own house. We met there to discuss his plan to liberate arable lands. He wanted to dismantle most suburbs, and large parts of the cities, creating "Free Agri-prize Zones." He proposed relocating the people in communities of his own design. They were energy and conservation-efficient, and were designed to make use of non-farmable terrain.

PRESIDENT BILL

tephanie, a writer and editor, was the first U.S. Cabinet secretary in history who could type 120 words per minute. I chose her to be Secretary of the Interior and charged her with restoring the country, within reason, to its original, natural state.

After some research, however, she concluded there was no particular "original state." True to the ideological spirit of my administration, she randomly picked a geologic period, the Late Cretaceous. At that time, she pointed out, the middle of the country was covered by a vast, warm, shallow ocean. ★ ★ ★ ★

PRESIDENT BILL

Of all my Cabinet ★ ★ *officers my secretary of state was the closest to being a government insider. Both Dan and his wife Olga (now assistant secretary of state) were real foreign service officers, and they had actually been abroad once. Snide rumors spread that Dan was upset merely because I invited Arafat to be a house guest and told Gorbachev we didn't need to verify Soviet disarmament. Also, allegedly, Dan was criticized within my administration for not being ideologically pure. He held a press conference to firmly deny the reports.* ★

PRESIDENT BILL

Susan, my domestic ★ adviser, and her husband Dean, Securities and Exchange Commission chairman, had us over for pizza, a video, and a talk. They were worried that I was alienating people, especially when I said that I supported creating a vast, warm, inland sea in order to "show those conservative Midwesterners what being in the 'mainstream' is really like." Susan urged me to make a speech and say I was the president of all the people, a respecter of all viewpoints. We needed, she said, a reassuring slogan to promote my aims for the country.

PRESIDENT BILL

I was disgusted when Congress tried to give itself a pay raise. The current congressional salary was three times the income my wife and I earned together before I became president. Worse, many congresspeople were rich to begin with. So I proposed a revised pay-scale plan. The annual salary of each congressperson would be equal to the yearly income of his or her poorest constituent. That would result in speedy social reforms, I thought. The congressional leadership was not in favor of my plan, and tried to persuade me to drop it. ★

PRESIDENT BILL

There were some odd scenes at the Capitol immediately following the congressional pay-cut. But, with each legislator's salary tied to the income of his or her poorest constituent, soon there was a rush to raise the minimum wage to $25 an hour, and to pass a comprehensive full-employment act. It proved to be the most productive period in the history of Congress. There were a few regrettable incidents, such as some attempts to forcibly remove poor people to other congressional districts, but, overall, the pay-cuts inspired many much-needed reforms.

PRESIDENT BILL

Among the new federal departments and positions I established were those of Folk Czar and Secretary of Humor. For the latter I wanted a person of the people, someone from beyond the Beltway, that circle of highway that separated bureaucratic Washington from real America. Out there, where people made their livings by muscle and sweat, was the cradle of that national treasure -- our country's humor. My wife assured me her brother John would be perfect for the job, and with a little coaching he could be confirmed quickly by Congress.

M ⊙ PRESIDENT BILL ⊗

My brother-in-law ★ ★ John's confirmation hearing was speedy. I had two reasons to appoint him head of the Department of Humor. First, my wife told me to give him a job. Second, his experience qualified him to administer the DOH's National Practical Joke Program. For instance, John once disassembled his best friend's Jeep, broke into the friend's house, and re-assembled the vehicle in the living room. The confirmation committee was charmed with John's jokes and stories. They easily discounted the sole witness against him, his former best friend. ★ ★

PRESIDENT BILL

leefully, I turned ★ ★ a reformist eye to the tax system that was so obviously devised by a clique of left-brained mathematicians, forcing normal people to hire accountants to do their taxes. It was, in short, a system that oppressed right-brained creative citizens. My new tax code was fair and simple. Instead of filing any forms, Americans would simply draw a self-portrait, or compose a poem, which was taxed on its artistic merit. The worse it was, the more tax. Naturally, the talentless could hire an artist for the job -- at very steep rates.

⊙ PRESIDENT BILL ⊗

The toughness of my ★ administration's environmental laws became evident when a super-tanker ran aground, spilling millions of gallons of oil into a pristine Alaskan bay. Despite the efforts of the oil company to scapegoat the tanker captain, the EPA arrested the company's top executives, and seized its tanker fleet.

The executives were meted out a punishment commensurate with the environmental destruction they had wreaked. The tankers were used by the new Navy, formerly the Greenpeace organization, for target practice. They used live ammunition. ★

41

▷ ⊕ PRESIDENT BILL ⚙

aycare was a priority of my administration. As most people's child care was provided at home, often by illegal aliens, we left those arrangements as they were, except the pay was taken over by government. Because of the shortage of care providers, we waived the need for alien work permits. Still, shortages persisted and parents were driven to offer extra wages for the best workers. We felt fortunate having such good, dependable care for the First Child. We were confident that Evita, the Vice President/Day Care Provider was not likely to get a better offer. ★ ★ ★

42

W ⊛ PRESIDENT BILL ⊛

We were thrown into ★ both a national and family crisis when Evita, the Vice President/Day Care Provider quit. A lawyer couple lured her away with more pay, shorter hours, and five years guaranteed employment. They pointed out that her term with us would last only four years. They could not offer her such impressive benefits, but she said that she was getting tired of the fuss, anyway. The Secret Service made her relatives nervous, she said, and the pressure of being a heartbeat away from such awesome responsibility was "bad for stomach."

☉ PRESIDENT BILL ⊗

Our former Vice President/Day Care Provider was leaving us for a quieter, better-paying position as a live-in suburban nanny. Replacing her was going to be tough. Fortunately, our ads received a large response. My advisors, concerned that the country was without a vice president, convinced me to solve the crisis quickly with a lottery, choosing at random from the applicants. After all, I had been selected to office by lottery, and I had founded randomocracy. Of course, for national security reasons, we screened all applicants first. ★ ★

PRESIDENT BILL

The media claimed that my administration had been braked to a standstill by the vice-presidential crisis, that it was ignoring pressing domestic and international issues. I held a press conference to dispute that. Simply because we were in the midst of arranging a lottery for a new Vice President/Day Care Provider did not mean we were neglecting the governance of the nation. In my speech I sidestepped the vice-presidential crisis, I avoided lengthy statements on policy and reforms. Instead, I addressed an issue of deep personal concern to me.

⊗ PRESIDENT BILL ⊗

I was a fanatic on few subjects. The main exception was the subject of beer. I did tend to go on about it. But, then, it was a fascinating topic. Unfortunately, America was largely a beer-illiterate nation. It was my duty, therefore, to educate and to set an example. So, I spoke to the nation. I told them that, as with many things, corporations and a big-and-bland-is-better mentality had subverted America's tastebuds. "Beer is like bread," I said. "There's the dark, hearty stuff from the local bakery, or there's the white, carcinogenic junk from the supermarket." ★

46

○PRESIDENT BILL

Cabinet meetings were informal. Since they were about the only times we got to see our friends we often combined meetings with other occasions, usually baby showers. They were always potluck. Sometimes we'd play a little music. First, however, we addressed vital domestic and world issues. For instance, we discussed the upcoming lottery for Vice President/Day Care Provider, the legalization of drugs, the institution of a draft for the EPA, VISTA, and the Peace Corps. Eventually, we always seemed to get around to one particular domestic issue. ★ ★ ★

Panama was created ★ by the U.S. When Colombia objected to our canal scheme in 1903, we instigated a revolution on its isthmus. The new nation handed over the Panama Canal Zone, which amounted to a U.S. colony. This was inexcusable for a country such as ours, founded on anti-colonialism. Now, though we were gradually relinquishing the Zone, Panama was ruled by a despot. Many decried his drug involvement, but, heck, I experimented in my wilder days, too. Still, on principle, I ordered Panama be returned to Colombia. But first, I sent in EPA troops.

PRESIDENT BILL

I was strongly for ★ ★ elderly people's rights. Before my selection as president I had to watch my grandmother Luanne being patronized and pushed around as her faculties diminished. Just because she was half-blind, nearly deaf, some-what unsteady, and a little forgetful, the county social workers didn't want to bother maintaining her independently in her familiar little home. No one in the family lived close enough to help or could pay $140 a day to put her in a good nursing facility. So she had to go to a county home. Then I became president. ★ ★ ★

PRESIDENT BILL

When I liberated my grandmother Luanne from the county nursing home, I tried to find a better place for her. She didn't want to live in a nice retirement home, or a senior's group home, or a regular house with private nursing-care. She didn't want to be institutionalized, period. Despite her age she insisted she could live independently, she didn't even want to live with us. Not that we had room for her anyway, as we spent most of our time at our small Takoma Park residence instead of the White House. So, there seemed to be only one solution. ★ ★ ★ ★ ★

PRESIDENT BILL

I was against the ★ ★ callous institutionalizing of elderly people. They were shamefully pushed out of the way when they became the slightest bit inconvenient to our youth-oriented society. My own grandmother, aged 90, served as an example to the nation. She lived independently in the White House with no nursing care, servants, or even Meals on Wheels. She overcame her limited hearing, sight, and memory. We respected her right to live alone, but we visited her often and kept in touch by telephone. Sometimes, she asked for help with little errands ★

ur son, the second first child, was born in a hospital birthing room. Mary used no pain killers, just a pot of raspberry tea. In natural childbirth the mother strives to achieve a relaxed, trance-like state. The father assumes a "coach" role, directing the mother's breathing, massaging her back, and giving encour-agement. We were al-lowed an assistant coach, a recent but close friend who flew in for the occa-sion. We named the baby, choosing from among the thousands of suggestions sent in by loyal citizens. We named him "Ran-dom," "Randy" for short.

PRESIDENT BILL

I was pleased that Random, our newborn second child, was a male, but I was annoyed with the many unenlightened comments we got from people, even from friends and family. I heard several remarks to the effect that I now had a child to take to baseball games or fishing trips, as though my eldest, a girl, was ineligible for such activities. Then there were the presents: guns, footballs, and trucks. Fortunately, as president, when I became annoyed I had a constructive outlet; I simply addressed the nation on television and got it out of my system.

53

PRESIDENT BILL

The choosing of the vice president was a great lesson in randomocracy. I appointed my previous vice president by picking the first person who walked through the Oval Office door. It turned out to be our day-care provider, Evita. Combining thus the positions of vice president and day-care provider was a stroke of serendipitous genius. Unfortunately, the day-care market being what it was, Evita was lured away by a better-paying job. We screened several applicants for the vice president/day-care provider position, then held a lottery to choose one. ★

A ◎ PRESIDENT BILL ⊗

Again, random ★ ★ ★ selection proved superior to elections. Our vice-president/day-care provider-select, Wayde, was a fine choice. He was a fervent randomocratist, he belonged to many progressive and liberal organizations, and he was a teacher. Granted, he taught computer programming, not preschool. But he had 15 nieces and nephews and played "a mean game of horsey." To tell the truth, we weren't sure how his application slipped through the screening process, but, the lottery was nationally televised, so we welcomed him warmly.

◉ PRESIDENT BILL ◈

*D*espite Mary's fears ★ about a man taking care of our children, Wayde, the new vice president/ day care provider, seemed fit for the job. The children were happy, Mary and I were able to attend to matters of state without having to wait for nap-times, and for the first time in American history, the vice president was being useful instead of sitting on a bunch of make-work commissions or moping around the Executive Office Building. The only sour note was from the reactionary media claiming the vice presidential lottery was somehow rigged. ★ ★ ★

It's a PLOT (and about time)! WHO is the Mystery Woman?

PRESIDENT BILL

I dismissed the rumors that the vice-presidential lottery was fixed by hostile forces. Clearly, random selection was popular; the American people preferred it to the flawed election process.

Randomocracy's only enemies were former members of the electoral-industrial complex: public relations firms, advertising agencies, the media, debate sponsors, and political parties. The electoral system had provided them with power and wealth. They, in turn, had kept an upper-class, telegenic clique in office. But, I had nothing to fear from them now. ★ ★ ★ ★

For nearly a decade ★ the U.S. promised major financial aid to Poland on condition that the government legalize the independent union Solidarity and hold elections. Unfortunately, the Poles waited until my administration to meet the requirements. As randomocrats, who believed that random selection, not election, of officials was more just and more representative, we could hardly support the Polish reforms. But our new policy, to withhold aid until the Poles instituted a selectoral lottery, was an instant success. It galvanized and united the Polish people.

PRESIDENT BILL

Fortunately, war with Poland was averted. The Poles were angry with my administration simply for sticking to its principles of randomocracy. True, previous U.S. administrations had promised the Poles aid and trading agreements if they would hold elections, but, of course, my administration believed in lotteries, not elections. So, accordingly, we changed the guidelines to U.S. aid. We officially ignored their subsequent declaration of war, waiting for them to come to their senses and deal with us in more effective terms, which they did. ★ ★ ★ ★ ★

◉ PRESIDENT BILL ⊗

During the hostage ★ *crisis, Americans held rallies, burned Polish flags, hams, kielbasi, and Lech Walesa effigies, and they harassed Polish-Americans. Several state legislatures banned polka music. Of course, my ad-ministration's response was more measured. First, I called President Gorbachev. I told him he was too lenient on the upstart Poles. I said we wouldn't blame him a bit for sending in tanks. Gorbachev said he regretted that his tanks were all being washed at the time. In the end, I personally went to Poland to negotiate the hostages' release.* ★ ★

60

W ⊙ PRESIDENT BILL ⊗

We were disturbed by ★ de-stabilizing events in China, where students were agitating for democracy. We worried about trade agreements and the balance of power, but also ideology. We stated that while we supported free speech, we felt the students were misguided. Democracy, a failure in our own country, only led to rule by the electable class: rich, aggressive, telegenic, power-hungry individuals. Elections were a hoax, only random selection of officials achieved just, equal representation. Covertly, we sent in a crack team of randomocratic agents.

61

PRESIDENT BILL

As hard-working and ★ frugal a president as I was, I still needed a vacation now and then. Because I insisted that my executive salary be equal to my pre-presidential earnings, we had limited funds for travel and accommodations. So, we just used the same resources we used before I was selected president. The first family drove to my brother-in-law John's house in a small Southern beach town. He could hardly refuse, as I had appointed him secretary of humor. Indeed, he and his wife, Charity, were as pleased to see us as we were to see them. ★ ★

PRESIDENT BILL

I never understood my brother-in-law's popularity. When the first family vacationed at his home near the beach, the press gave John most of its attention. He made headlines just slipping on a banana peel and throwing out his back. Admittedly, it was ironic, John being the secretary of humor. But, aside from that, I could not fathom how, with the presence of myself, truly the first people's president, daily enacting progressive, populist programs, the interviewers and photographers seemed more interested in John's silly good-old-boy antics. ★

PRESIDENT BILL

When the Supreme ★ ★ Court decided that burning the flag was a lawful expression of free speech, several congresspeople tried to exploit the issue. Wrapping themselves in Old Glory, they proposed legislation, even a constitutional amendment, that would make flag-burning a crime. Immediately, I ordered the development of the B-2 Combustible Flag. A great, but costly, technological leap forward, the flag was solar- and wind-powered, equipped with delicate sensors that caused the flag to burst into flame when approached within 30 feet by a politician. ★

⊙ PRESIDENT BILL ⊗

I tried to resist the ★ ★ Washington, D.C., game of political deal-cutting, but my aides said my costly B-2 Combustible Flag program was facing congressional resistance. To bolster support they invited some of the most reactionary members of Congress to a White House social gathering. They insisted on inviting a powerful senator who was trying to censor the arts by cutting their federal funding. He was hysterical about some recent museum exhibits. One contained homoerotic photographs, another portrayed a cross immersed in urine. ★ ★

65

PRESIDENT BILL

As the B-2 Combustible Flag started burning up billions in cost overruns, it became increasingly difficult to fund it. There was little support in Congress for the development of a flag that bursts into flame when approached by a politician. The defense budget had already been diverted to social and environmental programs. The balanced-budget amendment prevented us from allocating new funds. And, additional taxes would have been enormously unpopular. So, ever resourceful and creative, my advisors and I devised a state-of-the-art fund-raising tool.

PRESIDENT BILL

I have always been ★ health conscious, especially when it comes to food. So, one of my administration's proudest moments came with the creation of the Federal Food Agency. The Agency was under the aegis of the Environmental Protection Army. Its role was to enforce tough new legislation, known as the Junk-Food Eradication Act, the centerpiece of our "War on Junk." The Food Agency field agents were revered by the health-minded, feared by the junk-food pushers. They came to be known popularly as the "F-Men." ★

PRESIDENT BILL

I addressed the ★ ★ ★ American people about substance abuse. Despite my administration's efforts to halt the pushers and cartels, this dangerous activity continued. It still permeated American society, beginning with casual use, often encouraged by friends or even parents. It broke my heart to see children as young as 2 or 3 using these substances, imperiling their health, risking addiction. Sadly, it was the minority communities that were the most inundated. That was why I was stepping up our War on Junk, concentrating, this time, on the users of junk food.

68

◉ PRESIDENT BILL ⊗

ur War on Junk ★ ★ opened on four fronts: prison-building, re-habilitation, education, and overseas interdiction. It was an overwhelming task for Federal Food Agency officers, the "F-men," but since the legalization of drugs, the entire Drug Enforcement Administration was sitting idle. We found plenty of work for it. The existing environmental prisons and re-education camps were full. Children were daily falling prey to the junk-food habit. And the borders were a joke to smugglers of the deadly product of the evil cacao bean. ★ ★ ★ ★ ★ ★ ★

PRESIDENT BILL

The reactionary press seized on events at the Department of Defense, calling them the "DUM scandals." It was all nonsense. First, it was no secret that I wanted to cut back DOD. One of my first acts had been to exchange DOD's budget and facilities with EPA's. I downgraded the department from Cabinet level, expanded its duties, and changed its title. It was true that I neglected for months to appoint a head of Defense and Urban Maintenance (DUM), but my eventual choice was a good one. Juan, at 14 the youngest of my appointments, was gung-ho. ★ ★

PRESIDENT BILL

Juan, my appointee to head Defense and Urban Maintenance (formerly the Defense Department) was at 14 the youngest member of my administration, but I had the utmost confidence in him. I knew him personally: He was my next-door neighbor. I knew he was a dependable worker because he had mowed my lawn since he was 10. He filled administrative positions at DUM with many of his friends, good people all. His executive assistant, Hannah, came from a very good family. But backstabbing military careerists labeled her staff the "brat pack." ★ ★

PRESIDENT BILL

*T*he so-called "DUM ★ scandals" unfolded in the media during the slow news days of summer. It was true that I had gutted the Department of Defense and appointed a teen-ager to head what was now Defense and Urban Maintenance (DUM). But the press reported that Juan and his "brat pack" had misappropriated or lost billions of dollars. In the fall Congress, smelling blood in the water, held committee hearings, bullying and abusing Juan, his executive assistant, Hannah, and the innocent, idealistic young people they had hired. ★ ★ ★ ★ ★ ★ ★ ★

PRESIDENT BILL

There was no Veterans Department in my administration. After all, most Vietnam War veterans were being well cared for in political re-education camps, following, of course, their war crimes trials. We did, however, have a secretary of conscientious objection. Randall's job was to provide generous benefits to former conscientious objectors and oversee the dismantling of the selective service. Like many of our generation of conscientious objectors, Randall was emotionally scarred by the experience -- the ostracism, the abuse, and the lack of recognition.

As an artist, I admired the design of the Vietnam Memorial. I despised the groups who proposed adding tacky flags and statues to it, which would ruin its artistic integrity. However, as a former peace activist, I was disappointed that the memorial honored only the 58,000 U.S. war-dead, an echo of the country's wartime xenophobia. Then, we worried only about "our boys," ignoring the massacre of Vietnamese civilians. Luckily, as a politically enlightened artist, I was qualified to make a small correction that would not compromise the memorial. ★ ★

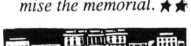

PRESIDENT BILL

I opposed building a ★ National Holocaust Museum on the Mall. It was the height of hypocrisy for America to denounce Germany's 10-year spate of atrocities when we had 300 years' worth of our own, beginning with the genocide of native Americans and slavery. So, my administration founded the Bureau of National Shame, which identified and preserved National Shameful Sites throughout the country: sites of massacres, lynchings, abuses, and environmental desecrations. It had a museum system on the Mall as extensive as the Smithsonian's. ★ ★

PRESIDENT BILL

The Cold War over, we needed only a minimal defense. Rather than maintain an expensive standing army, I initiated the Murphy's Defense Plan, based on Murphy's Law: "Whatever can go wrong, will." All military operations eventually bog down with blunders, equipment failures, and bureaucratic nonsense, so I abolished the military. If invaded, we would offer no resistance, just wait for Murphy's Law to take effect on the incurring force, which would collapse under its own ineptitude. Of course, the chances of an invasion were impossibly remote.

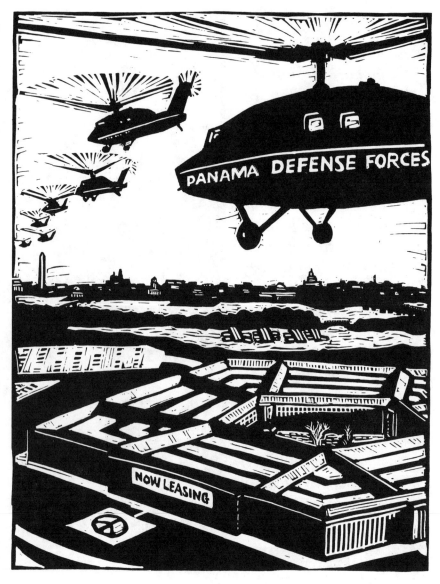

PRESIDENT BILL

Some Panamanians ★ were upset because, rectifying the United States' past imperialist errors, I had filled in the canal and returned their country to Colombia. Pursuing their own petty self-interests, the deposed Panamanians invaded the United States, scheming to capture and try me for supposed crimes against their country. Implementing my brilliant Murphy's Defense Plan, we offered only passive resistance, waiting for the enemy to bog down in its own mistakes. The First Family gracefully retired to the sanctuary of the National Cathedral. ★

PRESIDENT BILL

The Panamanian invaders were falling right into the subtle trap my Murphy's Defense set for them. Already they had blundered: Their attempt to capture and try me for trumped-up crimes had failed miserably. While my family and I were safe in sanctuary at the National Cathedral, the invaders set up a puppet regime, filling government posts with their cronies. All of them were criminals, freed by the Panamanians from prisons where my administration had put them for financing right-wing terrorists with shady arms and drug deals. ★ ★ ★ ★

PRESIDENT BILL

It was galling to have to sit in sanctuary, watching George Bush, the quisling, deliver the State of the Union address. But, I took heart. Most nations were outraged by Panama's invasion. NATO condemned it, and the Organization of American States said it would too, "as soon as we finish savoring the spectacle of Yankees getting a taste of their own medicine." Unfortunately, polls showed that less than a tenth of the American people were aware of the invasion and occupation of Washington, D.C., and the imposition of a puppet regime.

A ⊚ PRESIDENT BILL ⊗

At first, the ★ ★ ★ ★ ★ Panamanian invaders were gleeful that most Americans outside the occupied capital were apathetic to my fall from power. Then, the Panamanians found that Americans equally ignored the Bush puppet regime. Unable to extend their control beyond the capital area, and unable to capture me, they entered into talks. My skilled negotiating team maneuvered them into a complete withdrawal. In return, we traded some relatively unimportant territory, lands stolen from Spanish-speaking peoples in the first place.